A CHILD'S GARDEN
OF VERSES

R. L. STEVENSON

With an Introduction by
ELIZABETH GOUDGE

Illustrated by
HILDA GOLDWAG

COLLINS
LONDON AND GLASGOW

GENERAL EDITOR: G. F. MAINE

First published, 1885
This edition, 1955

Printed in Great Britain by
COLLINS CLEAR-TYPE PRESS

ROBERT LOUIS STEVENSON

ON a cold November night in the year 1850, a little boy was born in Edinburgh. He was Robert Louis Stevenson, and one day people all over the world were to know and love this name. His father, Thomas Stevenson, was a distinguished engineer, whose work was the designing and building of lighthouses up and down the coast. Many an exciting story he told his small son of storms and shipwrecks, of brave rescues, and gallant ships guided past the treacherous rocks by the beams of the warning lights.

Mrs. Stevenson was tall, slender and very lovely. The daughter of a minister, the Reverend Lewis Balfour of the nearby village of Colinton, she was not very strong, and though she loved her little son Louis very dearly, she had to leave him for much of the time in charge of his Nanny. This was no hardship for him, since Alison Cunningham—or "Cummy" as he called her—was a wonderful Nanny for any small boy. She was the most marvellous reader and had a wealth of thrilling tales of adventure, which she never tired of telling. Louis suffered from bronchitis and often had to stay in bed for days at a time till his feverish cough had spent itself. In the long restless nights when sleep would not come, and he lay tossing, listening to the wind moaning in the jet-black night, and wishing it were morning, Cummy would be at his bedside, comforting him, smoothing his pillows and chasing away his fears.

Some of Cummy's stories were rather frightening —stories of demons and devils, of a fearful God who punished sin with endless torture in the flames of hell. No wonder young Louis, with his vivid imagination, often had nightmares. Yet these stories were to help him in years to come; for they created in his mind a fabulous treasure-trove from which he drew many plots when writing his novels.

He was an only child and yet seldom lonely. He was never at a loss for something to play at, and loved all sorts of imaginative games. He would march his toy soldiers to battle across the great carpet plain, or if he was " sick and lay abed " he would sail his

> " . . . ships in fleets,
> All up and down among the sheets."

Sometimes he would just lie and watch the fire-light flickering on the walls and weave wonderful fantasies about smugglers lurking in shadowed caves, or highwaymen galloping along the moonlit roads.

Best of all he liked his toy theatre, which had been given to him when he was only six. Here he could make-believe as much as he wanted, with cut-out drawings of forests and castle ramparts for the back-grounds, and dashing figures of story-book heroes which could be moved jerkily but convincingly across the stage. These cut-outs were supplied " Penny plain and Twopence coloured " by a firm by the name of Skelt, and Louis was so enchanted with enacting fairy stories and exciting dramas in his theatre that he became, as G. K. Chesterton said, " a Skelt-drunken boy."

When he was seven he was sent to a prep school in Edinburgh, but persistent attacks of influenza and bronchitis kept him away for weeks, and so it was decided that he should be taught at home by his mother and private tutors. At the age of eleven he went to Edinburgh Academy; however, he was only there for about a year and a half, when his parents took him away and sent him to a small boarding-school near London. School-life did not really suit this dreamy, delicate little boy ; he was constantly being ragged and teased about his odd appearance, and because of his strange, rather shy manner he did not make friends easily. Though he was never a " cry-baby " and would courageously fight his tor-mentors, he did not fit into the rough-and-tumble of life at school and asked to be taken away. Finally when he was fourteen, he went to a small private school in Edinburgh.

His ambition was to become a writer. Starting at the age of six, with a short story about the life of Moses, which he wrote specially for his mother, he had been writing ever since—stories or articles for school magazines and later, plays which he produced with the help of his friends.

He had plenty of material, for in addition to drawing upon the world of story-telling and make-believe, every year he went with his parents on the most marvellous holidays. His mother was never strong and shared with Louis a longing for the warmth and sunshine which were seldom found amidst the damp mists and chill winds of Edinburgh. So, when Louis was twelve, they journeyed to London, to Stonehenge, to the Isle of Wight, and also to Germany. The next year they went wandering from Torquay, to the French Riviera, and thence to Italy. These were wonderful trips for Louis. He roamed through strange cities and feasted his eyes on unimagined splendours: the dark mysteries of the Catacombs; the slumbering power of mighty Vesuvius; the silent deserted streets and squares of Pompeii; the fabulous setting of Venice in its gliding waterways. All these impressions were gleaned and stored in the imagination of this young boy for whom travel was a never-ending delight. He was acutely observant and all he saw was preserved in his memory long afterwards.

Even during his years at Edinburgh University, he still travelled far and wide in the long vacations. His father was anxious that Louis should join him in lighthouse building, so when he was seventeen he began to study engineering. He tried to be interested in his father's profession, but it was of little use.

Though he came to love the wind-tossed seas and sailing in sturdy craft to and from the lighthouses, his heart was not in engineering. Eventually his father accepted this, though it was a great disappointment to him, and allowed Louis to become a student of law at the university. He worked hard and three years later, in 1875, passed his final law examinations.

All this time, however, he was still writing short stories, essays, articles and plays, and his idea of taking up a literary career remained unchanged. For this reason he never really practised law in earnest.

In September of the same year Louis and a young lawyer friend journeyed to France, sailing in two canoes from Antwerp to Brussels and up the Oise almost to the Seine. From their many breath-taking adventures Louis obtained valuable material for his first book, a travel book which he called *An Inland Voyage* (published in 1878). France fascinated him more and more on each returning visit. He met people of every profession and every nationality— artists, musicians, writers and sculptors from Belgium, America, Scotland and Scandinavia. He made friends with the most odd characters, sea-dogs, gamblers and tramps, and from these friendships gained a most intimate knowledge of the way other people thought and lived.

It was in France that he met Mrs. Fanny Osbourne, who was one day to become his wife. She had married an American when she was very young, but her ne'er-do-well husband had deserted her, leaving her with the care and upbringing of their three children. She was thirty-six, eleven years older than Louis when he met her—small and sturdy with vivid brown eyes set in a smooth, sun-burnt face, crowned by a mass of lovely black, curly hair. Louis fell deeply in love with her that autumn but they could not get married as her husband was still alive. However they wrote regularly to one another and whenever Louis was in Paris they met frequently.

Then Louis went on a solitary pony-trek through the lonely Cévennes Mountains, with a little donkey, which he named " Modestine," for his only companion. The vast solitude of the mountains made a deep impression on Louis and the grandeur of the scenery inspired him. He kept a diary of all that happened and of all his thoughts, hoping that Fanny might one day read it. Later, in 1879, it became a book, called *Travels with a Donkey*.

One day news came to him that Fanny was ill and very poor, far away in San Francisco, so Louis, against the advice of all his friends who said he was wrecking his career, and knowing how hurt and disappointed his parents would be, nevertheless packed his bag and in August 1879 set sail in the steamship *Devonia* for San Francisco and Fanny.

The journey there was like a nightmare, with storms and high winds, the passengers suffering both from seasickness and home-sickness, the decks often awash, and the sky dark and gloomy. The air inside the cabin was usually so heavy and stale that Louis preferred to stay on deck as much as possible even though it meant getting thoroughly soaked. All this was not at all good for someone who suffered from weak lungs, and by the time the *Devonia* docked at New York, Louis had begun to feel really ill. Then there was the interminably long train journey from New York to San Francisco, which at that time took eleven days. He had not much money and ate very little. The dry dust and the hot, stuffy atmosphere were equally bad for his health and soon his old hacking cough returned to torment him. Even when he arrived at San Francisco he still had a journey of several days on horseback before reaching Fanny at the village of Monterey where she was staying. She must have had difficulty in recognising this desperately thin, gaunt young man who had come half across the world because she was ill, and who himself was in far greater need of loving care and attention. She nursed him back to health and many weary months later the divorce proceedings against her husband were completed and she was free to marry Louis.

They were married on May 19th, 1880, when Louis was thirty, and Fanny was forty-one. They loved one another devotedly, and went to live with Fanny's son, Lloyd Osbourne, in the clear, high mountains above San Francisco. However they stayed there for only a few months and then decided to go to Scotland, urged by letters from Louis' parents who were longing to see them.

A warm-hearted welcome awaited them upon their arrival in Liverpool. Louis' father and mother were at the quayside, looking older and perhaps more care-worn, but delighted to see their son again and meet his wife. Fanny and Mrs. Stevenson took an immediate liking to one another and soon became firm friends, drawn together in their mutual care for Louis. Three months after his return to Scotland, his doctors discovered that he was suffering from tuberculosis, a dreaded disease of the lungs which at that time could seldom be completely cured. For the next seven years, Louis, his wife and his stepson moved from place to place seeking a climate which might be suitable to Louis' health. They went to Davos, high up in the Swiss Alps; they tried the Scottish Highlands too, and also a trip to Nice. Then they returned to England and stayed in Bournemouth, where the warm sunny days delighted him, but when it rained and he could not go out, he felt as if he were " living like a weevil in a biscuit."

He had many bouts of sickness and fever, days when he was depressed and peevish, and times when he lay so near to death's door that only the courage and determination of his little wife saved him. She cheered him up when he was sad, encouraged him in his writing, and nursed him when he was ill.

Louis describes her in one of his well-loved poems:

> "Trusty, dusky, vivid, true,
>   With eyes of gold and bramble-dew,
>   Steel-true and blade-straight,
>   The great artificer
>   Made my mate."

Once when he was very ill, lying in a dim, stuffy room, with nothing to do, he remembered all the magic and all the joys of his childhood and made them into those lovely poems which we read to-day in his famous book, *A Child's Garden of Verses*. Another day, he drew a chart of an imaginary island and christened it "Treasure Island." His stepson, Lloyd Osbourne, asked him to weave a story around it, and so every day he wrote a chapter of the dare-devil adventures of young Jim Hawkins, and the one-legged pirate, Long John Silver.

When these books were published they were immensely popular and the name of Robert Louis Stevenson became known throughout Great Britain and America. Some critics said of *Treasure Island* that it was "the best adventure story since *Robinson Crusoe*."

Louis, delighted with this success, started at once on another novel. This was the terrifying story of *Dr. Jekyll and Mr. Hyde*. Not long afterwards he wrote a wonderful adventure story, *Kidnapped*, a tale loved by boys of every generation, for it was written by one who never quite grew up, but always remained a boy at heart.

In May 1887 Louis' father died, and with his passing there was no longer any reason why the Stevenson family should stay in Britain. They all loved to travel, and the idea of a trip to America seemed the best way to take their minds off this grievous loss. Little did Louis realise as he waved good-bye to his friends, that he would never see his native land again.

For a very happy year this vagabonding family stayed in a little wooden cottage high up in the Adirondack mountains near the Canadian border. It was a severe winter, but Louis seemed to be able to stand up to the cold better than the others and used to take long walks through the fairy-like, snow-covered country, with its tall pine trees and high, white peaks looking very like a Christmas card.

In the spring, however, he became restless, and the thought of sailing to the South Seas, where the sun was always shining and the sea was always blue, appealed to him so much that he hired a schooner, the *Casco*, and taking all his family aboard, sailed off for " adventure." To Louis it was a boyish dream come true. For long idyllic months, they cruised among the islands of the South Seas, from the Marquesas, to Tahiti, and from there to Honolulu, the capital of Hawaii. Sometimes they would anchor in the shallow waters of a palm-fringed lagoon, where Louis made friends with the native chiefs, and they would all spend a few halcyon days on the coral shores, enchanted by the mystical scent of strange flowers, and the fantastically brilliant colours of the sun-kissed paradise.

One glorious morning they sailed into the port of Apia on the Samoan isles. It was a small place with straggling, native grass huts along the coast and densely wooded hills rising steeply behind them. At first Louis did not like the little village very much, but soon the tall dark palms, the silver beach and the whole quaint beauty of the island so delighted him that he became unwilling ever to leave. So Louis bought a piece of land six hundred feet up on the wooded side of a mountain, and they built a lovely house, which they named *Vailima*. The windows looked out across the deep turquoise blue of the bay and behind rose the high Vaea mountain.

They were very happy there and soon came to be known and respected by all the people of the island. The natives used to visit Louis telling him of all their troubles and grievances. With great understanding he would settle their quarrels and try to solve their worries, sending them away contented. When the natives learned that he wrote wonderful stories they called him *Tusitala* which means " teller of tales."

In his happy house, high up on this sun-lit island he concentrated once more on his writing. He produced a sequel to *Kidnapped*, called *Catriona*, and sent it home from Samoa; and then he started on what was perhaps the best of all his books though it was never finished, *Weir of Hermiston*. Every day he would work on it and in the evening with his mother, and Fanny, and his stepson Lloyd listening to him he would read it aloud and hear their criticisms.

He did much for the island and for its inhabitants and all he did was appreciated. He was wise and just and the natives soon realised that this white man was their friend. He improved the conditions in which they lived, wrote letters home about their disputes with the authorities and looked after them as if he were indeed their chieftain. In gratitude, the native chiefs built a road from *Vailima* to Apia, often digging with their own hands and at their own cost. And they called this road, the " Road of Loving Hearts."

Suddenly on an evening in December, 1894, Louis collapsed and died. He was mourned not only by his own family and his islanders but by people all over the world who had read and loved his books.

The natives of Samoa cut a zigzag path through the dense forests of the Vaea mountain and carried Louis' body to the very top, where he had always wanted to be buried. They carved the name " Tusitala " on his gravestone and laid him to rest beneath the poem which he had written:

> " Here he lies where he longed to be;
> Home is the sailor, home from the sea,
> And the hunter home from the hill."

MARGOT H. CLOW

CONTENTS

ROBERT LOUIS STEVENSON . 5
INTRODUCTION 21
Dedication 33
Bed in Summer 35
A Thought 36
At the Seaside 37
Young Night Thought 38
Whole Duty of Children 40
Rain 41
Pirate Story 42
Foreign Lands 44
Windy Nights 47
Travel 49
Singing 52
Looking Forward 53
A Good Play 54
Where Go the Boats? 55
Auntie's Skirts 58
The Land of Counterpane 59
The Land of Nod 61
My Shadow 63
System 66
A Good Boy 69
Escape at Bedtime 71
Marching Song 75
The Cow 76

Happy Thought 77
The Wind 79
Keepsake Mill 80
Good and Bad Children 83
Foreign Children 86
The Sun's Travels 89
The Lamplighter 91
My Bed is a Boat 93
The Moon 97
The Swing 98
Time to Rise 100
Looking-glass River 101
Fairy Bread 105
From a Railway Carriage 106
Winter-time 108
The Hayloft 111
Farewell to the Farm 112
North-West Passage:
    1. Good Night 115
    2. Shadow March 116
    3. In Port 118

THE CHILD ALONE

The Unseen Playmate 121
My Ship and I 125
My Kingdom 128
Picture-books in Winter 131
My Treasures 133
Block City 137
The Land of Story-books 139
Armies in the Fire 143
The Little Land 145

GARDEN DAYS

Night and Day   151
Nest Eggs   157
The Flowers   159
Summer Sun   161
The Dumb Soldier   165
Autumn Fires   168
The Gardener   171
Historical Associations   173

ENVOYS

To Willie and Henrietta   179
To My Mother   180
To Auntie   181
To Minnie   183
To My Name-Child   187
To Any Reader   189

INDEX TO FIRST LINES   191

INTRODUCTION

PERHAPS a preface should be an impersonal thing, but for me to write an impersonal preface to *A Child's Garden of Verses* is impossible, because it was the best beloved book of my own childhood, the first book I can remember having read to me and the first book from which I remember learning verses by heart. One of my earliest memories of being in a particular place is of being in bed in the night nursery, in the old house in the small cathedral town where I was born and spent my childhood, and looking out of the wide uncurtained window at the sky still full of light, and thinking how hard it was to have to be in bed by daylight with the world " so full of a number of things," and murmuring to myself,

> " And does it not seem hard to you,
> When all the sky is clear and blue,
> And I should like so much to play,
> To have to go to bed by day? "

Though I have not been in that night nursery since I was a child " Bed in Summer " takes me back there instantly. I can see the tree outside the window and my rag doll Violet with the darn on her nose, sitting at the foot of the bed, and outside the window, up in the sky at the top of the hill, there is the steeple of a church silhouetted black against the afterglow, and below it the tumbled uneven roofs of the old houses. The child I remember would watch until the light faded and the walls of the houses were patched with warm squares of lamplight, and then would come the lovely flowering of the lamps as the lamplighter came down the hill. And then presently the stars would come out, " the crowds of the stars . . . that glittered and winked in the dark," but their light was no lovelier than the light of the lamps that made a double chain of jewels down the street. It must be wonderful, I would think, to be a lamp-lighter, and then dazzled by the brightness I would turn over and look at the pictures that were " pasted on the wall " beside my bed, Christmas cards and advertisements, and pictures that Nanny and I had cut out of *Pears Annual* and stuck on ourselves with a flour paste that we had made on the kitchen stove.

" But the glory kept shining and bright in my eyes,
And the stars going round in my head."

Looking back from such a different world, through such a length of time, it seems that the sheltered happy childhoods of Victorian and Edwardian days had a very special magic. Childhood then was a world to itself. The door which shut off the nursery wing from the rest of the house made a very real dividing line between the life of the child and the adult. Behind it Nanny and her charges lived in their own

22

kingdom, from which they issued out at stated times
to shed the light of their countenance upon the outer
world. Visitors from this outer world, even mothers
and fathers, did not enter the kingdom without
hesitating at the portal and saying politely, " May
I come in, please, Nanny ? " And these same
visitors seemed gods and goddesses to the children,
revered and wonderful; it was not until we were
nearly adult ourselves that we discovered to our
astonishment that the grown-ups of the family had
a few faults. This state of things made for magic in
both worlds, the same sort of magic that an island
holds. There was a concentration of quietness and
orderliness within the world, a feeling of adventure
in leaving it, that fostered imagination and a sense of
beauty. Children did not grow up so quickly in
those days but their childhood was perhaps happier
and richer, and the enchantment of it has been perfectly caught by the verses in this book.

All the particular joys of those days are here;
R. L. S. has captured them all. First of all there is
Nanny herself, his beloved " Cummy." Thinking
of my own Nanny I can echo every word of his
dedication to her and greet every mention of her in
the verses with an ache of longing. Those wonderful
Nannies have gone now with that vanished world,
and we are the poorer for their going.

Then there are the barrel organ and the lamplighter,
the swing and the hayloft. In our quiet lives the

thrill of the lamplighter was followed next in order
of thrill by hearing the hurdie-gurdie coming down
the street. We would rush to the day nursery window
or the garden gate to catch a sight of his little red-
coated monkey and to dance to the sound of his
tunes. One is sorry for the child of to-day that he
has no lamplighter and no hurdie-gurdie. He has
a swing in the garden perhaps, but not often these
days, and the modern swing is not so wonderful as
ours, which was fastened to a very high branch on
a very tall tree, in our garden a huge cedar tree, and
had long ropes which swung you to such an immense
height that you could see right out of your own
kingdom into the wider world.

> " Up in the air and over the wall,
>   Till I can see so wide,
>   Rivers and trees and cattle and all
>   Over the countryside."

There was no joy to be compared with it except the
joy of the hayloft. I remember the one where
I played as a child, that quiet fragrant place with
the bales of hay and the scampering mice, the motes
of dust dancing in the golden sunshine that shone
through the small window, the Devonshire pony
munching in his stall below beside the old governess
cart that took us so many miles through the narrow,
dusty white lanes that wound their way up through
the high green Somersetshire hills. When we were
tired of playing games in the hay we would lie on

our fronts, our legs in the air, munching apples and reading.

> " O what a joy to clamber there,
>   O what a place for play,
>   With the sweet, the dim, the dusty air,
>   The happy hills of hay."

R. L. S. does not forget the joy of visiting Aunties, those very special Aunties who like the Nannies have now entirely vanished, females of grace and elegance who came on long visits and seemed to have nothing to do but play croquet and tell you wonderful stories, who dressed for dinner every evening and came to say good-night to you in the nursery in rustling silk dresses with posies of flowers in their belts. To watch such a creature leave the room was awe-inspiring and you gazed wide-eyed from your bath in front of the day nursery fire.

> " Whenever Auntie moves around,
>   Her dresses make a curious sound;
>   They trail behind her up the floor,
>   And trundle after through the door."

Of course there were a few flies in the magic ointment. We were disciplined. A modern child would be horrified at the severity of our training.

> " A child should always say what's true,
>   And speak when he is spoken to,
>   And behave mannerly at table:
>   At least as far as he is able."

If he didn't he was punished until he did. In that

there was not much joy for us; it was the grown-ups who benefited from the peaceful meals. And though it was delightful to go down to the drawing-room for an hour after tea, dressed in your best dress and coral necklace, and have *A Child's Garden of Verses* read aloud to you, and eat two (no more) sugared almonds out of the silver box, it was not so pleasant to go back again to the nursery afterwards in the semi-dark. It was a long journey and there was no electric light, and the candle in the hall gave only a ghostly glimmer. R. L. S. brings that fearful adventure to life again in the "North-West-Passage"; and he has not forgotten the exquisite joy of being on the other side of "the happy door" of your own safe, warm kingdom.

And yet it is the genius of R. L. S., as of all writers whose work lives, that he can catch not only the magic of a particular era but go deeper and catch the magic of existence itself. His work does not date. This book would not now be renewing its life to delight yet another generation of children, and the lovers of children, if it did not express perfectly the joy not only of a vanished childhood but the "glorious morning face" of the childhood of every generation. Childhood and joy should be synonymous, and R. L. S. expresses here the joys of childhood that have not changed since first children laughed and loved upon the earth, the joy in birds and beasts, flowers and stars, water, winds and sunshine, the joys of sleep and play, and the joy of the memory and the foretaste of the hidden things.

The child of these poems, like all children and all poets, and all those who retain the gift of wonder until they die, delights in analogy. The things that delight him in nature remind him of other delightful things, and his joy in them is doubled. At night, listening to the rise and fall of the gale, he hears the hoofs of a mysterious horse galloping backwards and forwards in the darkness. "A man goes riding by." When the wind is gentle it is "Like ladies' skirts across the grass," and the swish of it over the meadow makes waves of the rippling grasses. "And waves are on the meadows like there are at sea." When "the wonder of foam" has piled the fallen leaves together on the water they are floating castles to the child, sailing to a bourne a hundred miles away. The lovely things of nature are so real to him that he personifies them. The stars chase him indoors to bed, and he can talk to the wind as he talks to the cow who gives him cream "to eat with apple tart," or to the birds who make the April woods "merry with singing." The hours pass quickly with all these comrades, and then it is night and there is the adventure of sleep.

Most of us forget, as we get older, that sleep is an adventure. "To die will be an awfully big adventure," says Peter Pan, the boy who like the child of these poems has never grown up, and sleep, like

27

death, is a voyaging out into the unknown full of excitement and mystery. The night that sees him set sail in his bed like a little boat is to this boy " night divine." In the Land of Nod and in the Town of Sleep he sees armies and emperors and kings, and every kind of beast and man. He climbs the mountain sides of dreams and hears curious music. The adventures can be lonely and frightening at times, otherwise they would not be adventures, but they always have the same happy ending.

> " But when the day returns at last,
>   Safe in my room, beside the pier,
>   I find my vessel fast."

Children of every age are adventurous and their favourite games are always games of adventure, and do not change very much with the passing of the years. Boys climb trees now just as they always did, and march their armies to victory and sail upon voyages of exploration. Our modern cottages, flats and bungalows do not always provide suitable stairs upon which to build ships, but there are other places. I looked out of my window not long ago and saw almost an exact replica of " A Good Play." The two small boys who were staying with me had climbed to the roof of the wood shed, and with flag flying were going " A-sailing on the billows " there. They had dragged chairs to the top of the wood shed, and provisions from the larder, and it was really a better place than the stairs because there was no way of getting them down.

But there are other games which children delight in, more creative than adventurous, calling for a greater delicacy of imagination and bringing deeper powers of the soul into play. The verses that tell of these joys seem to me the loveliest in the book. " The Land of Counterpane " and " My Shadow " are surely two of the most delightful poems ever written, capturing so perfectly the joy of the imaginative escapes of childhood, and both of them leading on to the verses in " The Child Alone " which tell us the little that can be told of those two incommunicable experiences of childhood, the experiences of the Little Land and the Unseen Playmate. The giant upon the pillow hill is not yet in the Little Land, but looking at it from a distance. He has created his imaginative picture of it but he has not yet wanted to make himself small enough to walk under the trees in the dales and through the enchanted hills. In other poems we see him longing to be smaller. " I mean to grow as little as the dolly at the helm," he says in " My Ship and I," and in " Looking-glass River " the child sees the lovely little world under the water and longs to be there. In " My Kingdom " and " The Little Land " he has arrived. All of us can dimly remember going to that country

> " Where the clover-tops are trees,
> And the rain-pools are the seas."

R. L. S. calls it " The Land of Play," but though the journey there sometimes began as a game, as when in my own childhood I made a flower house for the fairies at the bottom of the garden and then went inside myself, it could become something much deeper. We did really escape out of this world. We recaptured for the moment something we had nearly lost. It was a gazing back to the coasts of the country that will not be seen again until the voyage is over and our ship comes back to where she started from.

The shadow that goes in and out with the child, and is seen, is not such a good playmate as the other who is not seen. It gave me a deep thrill when I first read " The Unseen Playmate " with understanding. For I was a lonely child and he came to me, as to all lonely children. That is all we remember, and if we remember more we could not describe what we remember, for " his is a picture you never could draw." But we know he is a real person. We may have lost him now but we shall find him again.

These verses, so full of joy in childhood, carry us on to the writer's joy in life. He had, we are told, " an invincible spirit of inward cheerfulness." The spontaneous joy of the happy child expressed in,

" The world is so full of a number of things,
 I'm sure we should all be as happy as kings,"

leads us to the resolved courageous joy of the man in

what must surely be the best beloved of all the adult poems,

> "If I have faltered more or less
> In my great task of happiness."

When we say of a writer that he can capture for us the magic of existence we mean that he is spiritually aware of the joy of existence, and that not in spite of, but because of suffering. R. L. S. suffered. Only a man whose life and work were rooted in suffering could have written "The Celestial Surgeon." He knew happiness to be not just a negative condition of immunity from pain, but a positive thing, a task, a creation of beauty hammered out by the courage of a man on the anvil of his pain. He learned that sensitiveness to beauty which can be taught by the raw nerves of illness, the value of sharp contrast which can make the swing from wretchedness to relief such sheer delight, and that pleasure in small things, "books, and my food, and summer rain," which a restricted life can give to those who refuse to make prison bars of their restrictions.

> "My body which my dungeon is,
> And yet my parks and palaces."

Because he set himself to be happy R. L. S. can make us happy. He is one of those writers who accompany us through life. The child enchanted with the verses in this book becomes the boy or girl thrilled to the marrow by *Kidnapped* and *Treasure*

31

Island, the man or woman delighting in all the novels and adult poems, in the *Vailima Letters* and the prayers that he wrote in his exile. He goes with us right through from youth to age, and then we find that we are back again where we started, with *A Child's Garden of Verses,* and perhaps they are the best after all.

> " Bright is the ring of words
>   When the right man rings them,
> Fair the fall of songs
>   When the singer sings them.
> Still they are carolled and said—
>   On wings they are carried—
> After the singer is dead
> And the maker buried."

ELIZABETH GOUDGE

Dedication

For the long nights you lay awake
And watched for my unworthy sake:
For your most comfortable hand
That led me through the uneven land:
For all the story-books you read,
For all the pains you comforted,
For all you pitied, all you bore,
In sad and happy days of yore:—
My second Mother, my first Wife,
The angel of my infant life—
From the sick child, now well and old,
Take, nurse, the little book you hold!

And grant it, Heaven, that all who read
May find as dear a nurse at need,
And every child who lists my rhyme,
In the bright fireside, nursery clime,
May hear it in as kind a voice
As made my childish days rejoice!

R. L. S.

BED IN SUMMER

In winter I get up at night
And dress by yellow candle-light.
In summer, quite the other way,
I have to go to bed by day.

I have to go to bed and see
The birds still hopping on the tree,
Or hear the grown-up people's feet
Still going past me in the street.

And does it not seem hard to you,
When all the sky is clear and blue,
And I should like so much to play,
To have to go to bed by day?

A THOUGHT

It is very nice to think
The world is full of meat and drink,
With little children saying grace
In every Christian kind of place.

AT THE SEASIDE

When I was down beside the sea
A wooden spade they gave to me
   To dig the sandy shore.
My holes were empty like a cup,
In every hole the sea came up
   Till it could come no more.

YOUNG NIGHT THOUGHT

All night long, and every night,
When my mamma puts out the light,
I see the people marching by,
As plain as day, before my eye.

Armies and emperors and kings,
All carrying different kinds of things,
And marching in so grand a way,
You never saw the like by day.

So fine a show was never seen
At the great circus on the green;
For every kind of beast and man
Is marching in that caravan.

At first they move a little slow,
But still the faster on they go,
And still beside them close I keep
Until we reach the town of Sleep.

WHOLE DUTY OF CHILDREN

A child should always say what's true,
And speak when he is spoken to,
And behave mannerly at table:
At least as far as he is able.

RAIN

The rain is raining all around,
  It falls on field and tree,

It rains on the umbrellas here,
  And on the ships at sea.

PIRATE STORY

Three of us afloat in the meadow by the swing,
  Three of us aboard in the basket on the lea.
Winds are in the air, they are blowing in the
    spring,
  And waves are on the meadows like the waves
    there are at sea.

Where shall we adventure, to-day that we're
    afloat,
  Wary of the weather and steering by a star ?
Shall it be to Africa, a-steering of the boat,
  To Providence, or Babylon, or off to Malabar?

Hi ! but here's a squadron a-rowing on the sea—
  Cattle on the meadow a-charging with a roar !
Quick, and we'll escape them, they're as mad as
    they can be.
  The wicket is the harbour and the garden is
    the shore.

FOREIGN LANDS

Up into the cherry-tree
Who should climb but little me ?
I held the trunk with both my hands
And looked abroad on foreign lands.

I saw the next-door garden lie,
Adorned with flowers before my eye,
And many pleasant places more
That I had never seen before.

I saw the dimpling river pass
And be the sky's blue looking-glass;
The dusty roads go up and down
With people tramping in to town.

If I could find a higher tree
Farther and farther I should see,
To where the grown-up river slips
Into the sea among the ships,

To where the roads on either hand
Lead onward into fairy land,
Where all the children dine at five,
And all the playthings come alive.

WINDY NIGHTS

Whenever the moon and stars are set,
　Whenever the wind is high,
All night long in the dark and wet,
　A man goes riding by.
Late in the night when the fires are out,
Why does he gallop and gallop about ?

Whenever the trees are crying aloud,
　And ships are tossed at sea,
By, on the highway, low and loud,
　By at the gallop goes he.
By at the gallop he goes, and then
By he comes back at the gallop again.

TRAVEL

I should like to rise and go
Where the golden apples grow;
Where below another sky
Parrot islands anchored lie,
And, watched by cockatoos and goats,
Lonely Crusoes building boats;
Where in sunshine reaching out
Eastern cities, miles about,
Are with mosque and minaret
Among sandy gardens set,
And the rich goods from near and far
Hang for sale in the bazaar;
Where the Great Wall round China goes,
And on one side the desert blows,
And with bell and voice and drum,
Cities on the other hum;

Where are forests, hot as fire,
Wide as England, tall as a spire,
Full of apes and coco-nuts
And the negro hunters' huts;
Where the knotty crocodile
Lies and blinks in the Nile,
And the red flamingo flies
Hunting fish before his eyes;

Where in jungles, near and far,
Man-devouring tigers are,
Lying close and giving ear
Lest the hunt be drawing near,
Or a comer-by be seen
Swinging in a palanquin;
Where among the desert sands
Some deserted city stands,
All its children, sweep and prince,
Grown to manhood ages since,
Not a foot in street or house,
Not a stir of child or mouse,
And when kindly falls the night,

In all the town no spark of light.
There I'll come when I'm a man
With a camel caravan;
Light a fire in the gloom
Of some dusty dining-room;
See the pictures on the walls,
Heroes, fights and festivals;
And in a corner find the toys
Of the old Egyptian boys.

SINGING

Of speckled eggs the birdie sings
   And nests among the trees;
The sailor sings of ropes and things
   In ships upon the seas.

The children sing in far Japan,
   The children sing in Spain;
The organ with the organ man
   Is singing in the rain.

LOOKING FORWARD

When I am grown to man's estate
I shall be very proud and great,
And tell the other girls and boys
Not to meddle with my toys.

A GOOD PLAY

We built a ship upon the stairs
All made of the back-bedroom chairs,
And filled it full of sofa pillows
To go a-sailing on the billows.

We took a saw and several nails,
And water in the nursery pails;
And Tom said, " Let us also take
An apple and a slice of cake ";
Which was enough for Tom and me
To go a-sailing on, till tea.

We sailed along for days and days,
And had the very best of plays;
But Tom fell out and hurt his knee,
So there was no one left but me.

WHERE GO THE BOATS?

Dark brown is the river,
    Golden is the sand.
It flows along for ever,
    With trees on either hand.

Green leaves a-floating,
  Castles of the foam,
Boats of mine a-boating—
  Where will all come home?

On goes the river
  And out past the mill,
Away down the valley,
  Away down the hill.

Away down the river,
  A hundred miles or more,
Other little children
  Shall bring my boats ashore.

AUNTIE'S SKIRTS

Whenever Auntie moves around,
Her dresses make a curious sound;
They trail behind her up the floor,
And trundle after through the door.

THE LAND OF COUNTERPANE

When I was sick and lay a-bed,
I had two pillows at my head,
And all my toys beside me lay
To keep me happy all the day.

And sometimes for an hour or so
I watched my leaden soldiers go,
With different uniforms and drills,
Among the bed-clothes, through the hills;

And sometimes sent my ships in fleets
All up and down among the sheets;
Or brought my trees and houses out,
And planted cities all about.

I was the giant great and still
That sits upon the pillow-hill,
And sees before him, dale and plain,
The pleasant land of counterpane.

THE LAND OF NOD

From breakfast on all through the day
At home among my friends I stay;
But every night I go abroad
Afar into the land of Nod.

All by myself I have to go,
With none to tell me what to do—
All alone beside the streams
And up the mountain-sides of dreams.

The strangest things are there for me,
Both things to eat and things to see,
And many frightening sights abroad
Till morning in the land of Nod.

Try as I like to find the way,
I never can get back by day,
Nor can remember plain and clear
The curious music that I hear.

MY SHADOW

I have a little shadow that goes in and out with
    me,
And what can be the use of him is more than I
    can see.
He is very, very like me from the heels up to the
    head;
And I see him jump before me, when I jump
    into my bed.

The funniest thing about him is the way he likes
    to grow—
Not at all like proper children, which is always
    very slow;
For he sometimes shoots up taller like an india-
    rubber ball,
And he sometimes gets so little that there's none
    of him at all.

He hasn't got a notion of how children ought to
  play,
And can only make a fool of me in every sort of
  way.
He stays so close beside me, he's a coward you
  can see;
I'd think shame to stick to nursie as that shadow
  sticks to me !

One morning, very early, before the sun was up,
I rose and found the shining dew on every
  buttercup;
But my lazy little shadow, like an arrant sleepy-
  head,
Had stayed at home behind me and was fast
  asleep in bed.

SYSTEM

Every night my prayers I say,
And get my dinner every day;
And every day that I've been good,
I get an orange after food.

The child that is not clean and neat,
With lots of toys and things to eat,
He is a naughty child, I'm sure—
Or else his dear papa is poor.

A GOOD BOY

I woke before the morning, I was happy all the
    day,
I never said an ugly word, but smiled and stuck
    to play.

And now at last the sun is going down behind
    the wood,
And I am very happy, for I know that I've been
    good.

My bed is waiting cool and fresh, with linen
    smooth and fair,
And I must off to sleepsin-by, and not forget my
    prayer.

I know that, till to-morrow I shall see the sun
    arise,
No ugly dream shall fright my mind, no ugly
    sight my eyes,

But slumber hold me tightly till I waken in the
   dawn,
And hear the thrushes singing in the lilacs round
   the lawn.

ESCAPE AT BEDTIME

The lights from the parlour and kitchen shone
    out
  Through the blinds and the windows and bars;
And high overhead and all moving about,
  There were thousands of millions of stars.
There ne'er were such thousands of leaves on a
    tree,
  Nor of people in church or the Park,

As the crowds of the stars that looked down
   upon me,
   And that glittered and winked in the dark.

The Dog, and the Plough, and the Hunter, and
   all,
   And the star of the sailor, and Mars,
These shone in the sky, and the pail by the wall
   Would be half full of water and stars.
They saw me at last, and they chased me with
   cries,
   And they soon had me packed into bed;
But the glory kept shining and bright in my eyes,
   And the stars going round in my head.

MARCHING SONG

Bring the comb and play upon it!
  Marching, here we come!
Willie cocks his highland bonnet,
  Johnnie beats the drum.

Mary Jane commands the party,
  Peter leads the rear;
Feet in time, alert and hearty,
  Each a Grenadier!

All in the most martial manner
  Marching double-quick;
While the napkin like a banner
  Waves upon the stick!

Here's enough of fame and pillage,
  Great commander Jane!
Now that we've been round the village,
  Let's go home again.

THE COW

The friendly cow, all red and white,
   I love with all my heart:
She gives me cream with all her might,
   To eat with apple-tart.

She wanders lowing here and there,
   And yet she cannot stray,
All in the pleasant open air,
   The pleasant light of day;

And blown by all the winds that pass
   And wet with all the showers,
She walks among the meadow grass
   And eats the meadow flowers.

HAPPY THOUGHT

The world is so full
    of a number of things,
I'm sure we should all
    be as happy as kings.

THE WIND

I saw you toss the kites on high
And blow the birds about the sky;
And all around I heard you pass,
Like ladies' skirts across the grass—
    O wind, a-blowing all day long,
    O wind, that sings so loud a song!

I saw the different things you did,
But always you yourself you hid.
I felt you push, I heard you call,
I could not see yourself at all—
    O wind, a-blowing all day long,
    O wind, that sings so loud a song!

O you that are so strong and cold,
O blower, are you young or old?
Are you a beast of field and tree,
Or just a stronger child than me?
    O wind, a-blowing all day long,
    O wind, that sings so loud a song!

KEEPSAKE MILL

Over the borders, a sin without pardon,
  Breaking the branches and crawling below,
Out through the breach in the wall of the garden,
  Down by the banks of the river, we go.

Here is the mill with the humming of thunder,
  Here is the weir with the wonder of foam,
Here is the sluice with the race running under—
  Marvellous places, though handy to home!

Sounds of the village grow stiller and stiller,
  Stiller the note of the birds on the hill;
Dusty and dim are the eyes of the miller,
  Deaf are his ears with the moil of the mill.

Years may go by, and the wheel in the river
  Wheel as it wheels for us, children, to-day,
Wheel and keep roaring and foaming for ever
  Long after all of the boys are away.

Home from the Indies, and home from the ocean,
  Heroes and soldiers we all shall come home;
Still we shall find the old mill-wheel in motion,
  Turning and churning that river to foam.

You with the bean that I gave when we
      quarrelled,
  I with your marble of Saturday last,
Honoured and old and all gaily apparelled,
  Here we shall meet and remember the past.

GOOD AND BAD CHILDREN

Children, you are very little,
And your bones are very brittle;
If you would grow great and stately,
You must try to walk sedately.

You must still be bright and quiet,
And content with simple diet;
And remain, through all bewild'ring,
Innocent and honest children.

Happy hearts and happy faces,
Happy play in grassy places—
That was how, in ancient ages,
Children grew to kings and sages.

But the unkind and the unruly,
And the sort to eat unduly,
They must never hope for glory—
Theirs is quite a different story!

Cruel children, crying babies,
All grow up as geese and gabies,
Hated, as their age increases,
By their nephews and their nieces.

FOREIGN CHILDREN

Little Indian, Sioux or Crow,
Little frosty Eskimo,
Little Turk or Japanee,
O! don't you wish that you were me?

86

You have seen the scarlet trees
And the lions over seas;
You have eaten ostrich eggs,
And turned the turtles off their legs.

Such a life is very fine,
But it's not so nice as mine;
You must often, as you trod,
Have wearied *not* to be abroad.

You have curious things to eat,
I am fed on proper meat;
You must dwell beyond the foam,
But I am safe and live at home.

Little Indian, Sioux or Crow,
Little Frosty Eskimo,
Little Turk or Japanee,
O! don't you wish that you were me?

THE SUN'S TRAVELS

The sun is not a-bed when I
At night upon my pillow lie;
Still round the earth his way he takes,
And morning after morning makes.

While here at home, in shining day,
We round the sunny garden play,
Each little Indian sleepy-head
Is being kissed and put to bed.

And when at eve I rise from tea,
Day dawns beyond the Atlantic Sea,
And all the children in the West
Are getting up and being dressed.

THE LAMPLIGHTER

My tea is nearly ready
  and the sun has left the sky;
It's time to take the window
  to see Leerie going by;
For every night at tea-time
  and before you take your seat,
With lantern and with ladder
  he comes posting up the street.

Now Tom would be a driver
  and Maria go to sea,
And my papa's a banker
  and as rich as he can be;
But I, when I am stronger
  and can choose what I'm to do,
O Leerie, I'll go round at night
  and light the lamps with you!

For we are very lucky,
  with a lamp before the door,
And Leerie stops to light it
  as he lights so many more;
And O! before you hurry by
  with ladder and with light,
O Leerie, see a little child
  and nod to him to-night!

MY BED IS A BOAT

My bed is like a little boat;
   Nurse helps me in when I embark;
She girds me in my sailor's coat
   And starts me in the dark.

At night, I go on board and say
　　Good-night to all my friends on shore;
I shut my eyes and sail away
　　And see and hear no more.

And sometimes things to bed I take,
　　As prudent sailors have to do;
Perhaps a slice of wedding-cake,
　　Perhaps a toy or two.

All night across the dark we steer:
　　But when the day returns at last,
Safe in my room, beside the pier,
　　I find my vessel fast.

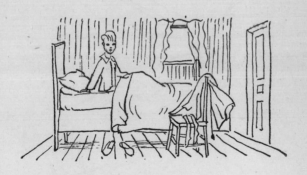

THE MOON

The moon has a face like the clock in the hall;
She shines on thieves on the garden wall,
On streets and fields and harbour quays,
And birdies asleep in the forks of the trees.

The squalling cat and the squeaking mouse,
The howling dog by the door of the house,
The bat that lies in bed at noon,
All love to be out by the light of the moon.

But all of the things that belong to the day
Cuddle to sleep to be out of her way;
And flowers and children close their eyes
Till up in the morning the sun shall rise.

THE SWING

How do you like to go up in a swing,
  Up in the air so blue?
Oh, I do think it the pleasantest thing
  Ever a child can do!

Up in the air and over the wall,
  Till I can see so wide,
Rivers and trees and cattle and all
  Over the countryside—

Till I look down on the garden green,
  Down on the roof so brown—
Up in the air I go flying again,
  Up in the air and down!

TIME TO RISE

A birdie with a yellow bill
Hopped upon the window sill.
Cocked his shining eye and said:
" Ain't you 'shamed, you sleepy-head ? "

LOOKING-GLASS RIVER

Smooth it slides upon its travel,
  Here a wimple, there a gleam—
    O the clean gravel!
    O the smooth stream!

Sailing blossoms, silver fishes,
  Paven pools as clear as air—
    How a child wishes
    To live down there!

We can see our coloured faces
   Floating on the shaken pool
      Down in cool places,
      Dim and very cool;

Till a wind or water wrinkle,
   Dipping marten, plumping trout,
      Spreads in a twinkle
      And blots all out.

See the rings pursue each other;
   All below grows black as night,
      Just as if mother
      Had blown out the light!

Patience, children, just a minute—
   See the spreading circles die;
      The stream and all in it
      Will clear by-and-by.

FAIRY BREAD

Come up here, O dusty feet!
   Here is fairy bread to eat.
Here in my retiring room,
   Children, you may dine
On the golden smell of broom
   And the shade of pine;
And when you have eaten well,
Fairy stories hear and tell.

FROM A RAILWAY CARRIAGE

Faster than fairies, faster than witches,
Bridges and houses, hedges and ditches;
And charging along like troops in a battle,
All through the meadows the horses and cattle:
All of the sights of the hill and the plain
Fly as thick as driving rain;
And ever again, in the wink of an eye,
Painted stations whistle by.

Here is a child who clambers and scrambles,
All by himself and gathering brambles;
Here is a tramp who stands and gazes;
And there is the green for stringing the daisies!
Here is a cart run away in the road
Lumping along with man and load;
And here is a mill, and there is a river:
Each a glimpse and gone for ever!

WINTER-TIME

Late lies the wintry sun a-bed,
A frosty, fiery sleepy-head;
Blinks but an hour or two; and then,
A blood-red orange, sets again.

Before the stars have left the skies,
At morning in the dark I rise;
And shivering in my nakedness,
By the cold candle, bathe and dress.

Close by the jolly fire I sit
To warm my frozen bones a bit;
Or with a reindeer-sled, explore
The colder countries round the door.

When, to go out, my nurse doth wrap
Me in my comforter and cap:
The cold wind burns my face, and blows
Its frosty pepper up my nose.

Black are my steps on silver sod;
Thick blows my frosty breath abroad;
And tree and house, and hill and lake,
Are frosted like a wedding-cake.

THE HAYLOFT

Through all the pleasant meadow-side
  The grass grew shoulder-high,
Till the shining scythes went far and wide
  And cut it down to dry.

These green and sweetly smelling crops
  They led in waggons home;
And they piled them here in mountain tops
  For mountaineers to roam.

Here is Mount Clear, Mount Rusty-Nail,
  Mount Eagle and Mount High;—
The mice that in these mountains dwell,
  No happier are than I!

O what a joy to clamber there,
  O what a place for play,
With the sweet, the dim, the dusty air,
  The happy hills of hay.

FAREWELL TO THE FARM

The coach is at the door at last;
The eager children, mounting fast
And kissing hands, in chorus sing:
Good-bye, good-bye, to everything!

To house and garden, field and lawn,
The meadow-gates we swang upon,
To pump and stable, tree and swing,
Good-bye, good-bye, to everything!

And fare you well for evermore,
O ladder at the hayloft door,
O hayloft where the cobwebs cling,
Good-bye, good-bye, to everything!

Crack goes the whip, and off we go;
The trees and houses smaller grow;
Last, round the woody turn we swing:
Good-bye, good-bye, to everything!

NORTH-WEST PASSAGE

1. *Good Night*

When the bright lamp is carried in,
The sunless hours again begin;
O'er all without, in field and lane,
The haunted night returns again.

Now we behold the embers flee
About the firelit hearth; and see
Our faces painted as we pass,
Like pictures, on the window-glass.

Must we to bed indeed? Well then,
Let us arise and go like men,
And face with an undaunted tread
The long black passage up to bed.

Farewell, O brother, sister, sire!
O pleasant party round the fire!
The songs you sing, the tales you tell,
Till far to-morrow, fare ye well!

2. Shadow March

All round the house is the jet-black night;
  It stares through the window-pane;
It crawls in the corners, hiding from the light,
  And it moves with the moving flame.

Now my little heart goes a-beating like a drum,
  With the breath of the Bogie in my hair;
And all round the candle the crooked shadows
    come
  And go marching along up the stair.

The shadow of the balusters, the shadow of the
  lamp,
  The shadow of the child that goes to bed—
All the wicked shadows coming, tramp, tramp,
  tramp,
  With the black light overhead.

3. *In Port*

Last, to the chamber where I lie
My fearful footsteps patter nigh,
And come from out the cold and gloom
Into my warm and cheerful room.

There, safe arrived, we turn about
To keep the coming shadows out,
And close the happy door at last
On all the perils that we past.

Then, when mamma goes by to bed,
She shall come in with tip-toe tread,
And see me lying warm and fast
And in the Land of Nod at last.

THE CHILD ALONE

THE UNSEEN PLAYMATE

When children are playing alone on the green,
In comes the playmate that never was seen.
When children are happy and lonely and good,
The Friend of the Children comes out of the
    wood.

Nobody heard him and nobody saw,
His is a picture you never could draw,
But he's sure to be present, abroad or at home,
When children are happy and playing alone.

He lies in the laurels, he runs on the grass,
He sings when you tinkle the musical glass;
Whene'er you are happy and cannot tell why,
The Friend of the Children is sure to be by!

He loves to be little, he hates to be big,
'Tis he that inhabits the caves that you dig;
'Tis he when you play with your soldiers of tin
That sides with the Frenchmen and never can
    win.

'Tis he, when at night you go off to your bed,
Bids you go to your sleep and not trouble your
    head;
For wherever they're lying, in cupboard or shelf,
'Tis he will take care of your playthings himself!

MY SHIP AND I

) it's I that am the captain of a tidy little ship,
  Of a ship that goes a-sailing on the pond;
nd my ship it keeps a-turning all around and
    all about;
ut when I'm a little older, I shall find the secret
    out
How to send my vessel sailing on beyond.

or I mean to grow as little as the dolly at the
    helm,
    And the dolly I intend to come alive;
And with him beside to help me, it's a-sailing I
    shall go,
t's a-sailing on the water, when the jolly breezes
    blow
    And the vessel goes a divie-divie dive.

) it's then you'll see me sailing through the
    rushes and the reeds,
    And you'll hear the water singing at the prow;
or beside the dolly sailor, I'm to voyage and
    explore,
o land upon the island where no dolly was
    before,
    And to fire the penny cannon in the bow.

MY KINGDOM

Down by a shining water well
I found a very little dell,
  No higher than my head.
The heather and the gorse about
In summer bloom were coming out,
  Some yellow and some red.

I called the little pool a sea;
The little hills were big to me;
  For I am very small.
I made a boat, I made a town,
I searched the caverns up and down,
  And named them one and all.

And all about was mine, I said,
The little sparrows overhead,
  The little minnows too.
This was the world and I was king;
For me the bees came by to sing,
  For me the swallows flew.

I played there were no deeper seas,
Nor any wider plains than these,
   No other kings than me.
At last I heard my mother call
Out from the house at even-fall,
   To call me home to tea.

And I must rise and leave my dell,
And leave my dimpled water well,
   And leave my heather blooms.
Alas! and as my home I neared,
How very big my nurse appeared,
   How great and cool the rooms!

PICTURE-BOOKS IN WINTER

Summer fading, winter comes—
Frosty mornings, tingling thumbs,
Window robins, winter rooks,
And the picture story-books.

Water now is turned to stone
Nurse and I can walk upon;
Still we find the flowing brooks
In the picture story-books.

All the pretty things put by,
Wait upon the children's eye,
Sheep and shepherds, trees and crooks,
In the picture story-books.

We may see how all things are,
Seas and cities, near and far,
And the flying fairies' looks,
In the picture story-books.

How am I to sing your praise,
Happy chimney-corner days,
Sitting safe in nursery nooks,
Reading picture story-books?

MY TREASURES

These nuts that I keep in the back of the nest
Where all my lead soldiers are lying at rest,
Were gathered in autumn by nursie and me
In a wood with a well by the side of the sea.

This whistle we made (and how clearly it
    sounds!)
By the side of a field at the end of the grounds.
Of a branch of a plane, with a knife of my own,
It was nursie who made it, and nursie alone!

The stone, with the white and the yellow and
    grey,
We discovered I cannot tell *how* far away;
And I carried it back although weary and cold,
For though father denies it, I'm sure it is gold.

But of all of my treasures the last is the king,
For there's very few children possess such a
    thing;
And that is a chisel, both handle and blade,
Which a man who was really a carpenter made.

BLOCK CITY

What are you able to build with your blocks?
Castle and palaces, temples and docks.
Rain may keep raining, and others go roam,
But I can be happy and building at home.

Let the sofa be mountains, the carpet be sea,
There I'll establish a city for me;
A kirk and a mill and a palace beside,
And a harbour as well where my vessels may ride.

Great is the palace with pillar and wall,
A sort of a tower on the top of it all,
And steps coming down in an orderly way
To where my toy vessels lie safe in the bay.

This one is sailing and that one is moored:
Hark to the song of the sailors on board!
And see on the steps of my palace, the kings
Coming and going with presents and things!

Now I have done with it, down let it go!
All in a moment the town is laid low.
Block upon block lying scattered and free,
What is there left of my town by the sea?

Yet as I saw it, I see it again,
The kirk and the palace, the ships and the men,
And as long as I live, and where'er I may be,
I'll always remember my town by the sea.

THE LAND OF STORY-BOOKS

At evening when the lamp is lit,
Around the fire my parents sit;
They sit at home and talk and sing,
And do not play at anything.

Now, with my little gun, I crawl
All in the dark along the wall,
And follow round the forest track
Away behind the sofa back.

There, in the night, where none can spy,
All in my hunter's camp I lie,
And play at books that I have read
Till it is time to go to bed.

These are the hills, these are the woods,
These are my starry solitudes;
And there the river by whose brink
The roaring lions come to drink.

I see the others far away
As if in firelit camp they lay,
And I, like to an Indian scout,
Around their party prowled about.

So, when my nurse comes in for me,
Home I return across the sea,
And go to bed with backward looks
At my dear land of Story-books.

ARMIES IN THE FIRE

The lamps now glitter down the street;
Faintly sound the falling feet;
And the blue even slowly falls
About the garden trees and walls.

Now in the falling of the gloom
The red fire paints the empty room:
And warmly on the roof it looks,
And flickers on the backs of books.

Armies march by tower and spire
Of cities blazing, in the fire;
Till as I gaze with staring eyes,
The armies fade, the lustre dies.

Then once again the glow returns;
Again the phantom city burns;
And down the red-hot valley, lo!
The phantom armies marching go!

Blinking embers, tell me true,
Where are those armies marching to,
And what the burning city is
That crumbles in your furnaces!

THE LITTLE LAND

When at home alone I sit
And am very tired of it,
I have just to shut my eyes
To go sailing through the skies—
To go sailing far away
To the pleasant Land of Play;
To the fairy land afar
Where the Little People are;
Where the clover-tops are trees,
And the rain-pools are the seas,
And the leaves like little ships
Sail about on tiny trips;
And above the daisy tree
  Through the grasses,
High o'erhead the Bumble Bee
  Hums and passes.

In that forest to and fro
I can wander, I can go;
See the spider and the fly,
And the ants go marching by
Carrying parcels with their feet
Down the green and grassy street.
I can in the sorrel sit,
Where the ladybird alit.
I can climb the jointed grass,
    And on high
See the greater swallows pass
    In the sky,
And the round sun rolling by
Heeding no such things as I.

Through that forest I can pass
Till, as in a looking-glass,
Humming fly and daisy tree
And my tiny self I see,
Painted very clear and neat
On the rain-pool at my feet.
Should a leaflet come to land
Drifting near to where I stand,
Straight I'll board that tiny boat
Round the rain-pool sea to float.

Little thoughtful creatures sit
On the grassy coasts of it.
Little things with lovely eyes
See me sailing with surprise.
Some are clad in armour green—
(These have sure to battle been!)—
Some are pied with every hue,
Black and crimson, gold and blue;
Some have wings and swift are gone;
But they all look kindly on.

When my eyes I once again
Open, and see all things plain:
High bare walls, great bare floor;
Great big knobs on drawer and door;
Great big people perched on chairs,
Stitching tucks and mending tears,
Each a hill that I could climb,
And talking nonsense all the time—
    O dear. me,
    That I could be
A sailor on the rain-pool sea,
A climber in the clover tree,
And just come back, a sleepy-head,
Late at night to go to bed.

GARDEN DAYS

NIGHT AND DAY

When the golden day is done,
  Through the closing portal,
Child and garden, flower and sun,
  Vanish all things mortal.

As the blinding shadows fall,
  As the rays diminish,
Under evening's cloak, they all
  Roll away and vanish.

Garden darkened, daisy shut,
  Child in bed, they slumber—
Glow-worm in the highway rut,
  Mice among the lumber.

In the darkness houses shine,
    Parents move with candles;
Till, on all, the night divine
    Turns the bedroom handles.

Till at last the day begins
    In the east a-breaking,
In the hedges and the whins
    Sleeping birds a-waking.

In the darkness shapes of things,
    Houses, trees, and hedges,
Clearer grow; and sparrows' wings
    Beat on window ledges.

These shall wake the yawning maid;
  She the door shall open—
Finding dew on garden glade
  And the morning broken.

There my garden grows again
　　Green and rosy painted,
As at eve behind the pane
　　From my eyes it fainted.

Just as it was shut away,
　　Toy-like, in the even,
Here I see it glow with day
　　Under glowing heaven.

Every path and every plot,
　　Every bush of roses,
Every blue forget-me-not
　　Where the dew reposes.

Up! " they cry, " the day is come
　　On the smiling valleys;
We have beat the morning drum;
　　Playmate, join your allies! "

NEST EGGS

Birds all the sunny day
  Flutter and quarrel
Here in the arbour-like
  Tent of the laurel.

Here in the fork
  The brown nest is seated;
Four little blue eggs
  The mother keeps heated.

While we stand watching her,
  Staring like gables,
Safe in each egg are the
  Bird's little babies.

Soon the frail eggs they shall
  Chip, and upspringing
Make all the April woods
  Merry with singing.

Younger than we are,
  O children, and frailer,
Soon in blue air they'll be
  Singer and sailor.

We, so much older,
  Taller and stronger,
We shall look down on the
  Birdies no longer.

They shall go flying
  With musical speeches
High overhead in the
  Tops of the beeches.

In spite of our wisdom
  And sensible talking,
We on our feet must go
  Plodding and walking.

THE FLOWERS

All the names I know from nurse:
Gardener's garters, Shepherd's purse,
Bachelor's buttons, Lady's smock,
And the Lady Hollyhock.

Fairy places, fairy things,
Fairy woods where the wild bee wings,
Tiny trees for tiny dames—
These must all be fairy names!

Tiny woods below whose boughs
Shady fairies weave a house;
Tiny tree-tops, rose or thyme,
Where the braver fairies climb!

Fair are grown-up people's trees,
But the fairest woods are these;
Where if I were not so tall,
I should live for good and all.

SUMMER SUN

Great is the sun, and wide he goes
Through empty heaven without repose;
And in the blue and glowing days
More thick than rain he showers his rays.

Though closer still the blinds we pull
To keep the shady parlour cool,
Yet he will find a chink or two
To slip his golden fingers through

The dusty attic, spider-clad,
He, through the keyhole, maketh glad;
And through the broken edge of tiles,
Into the laddered hayloft smiles.

Meantime his golden face around
He bares to all the garden ground,
And sheds a warm and glittering look
Among the ivy's inmost nook.

Above the hills, along the blue,
Round the bright air with footing true,
To please the child, to paint the rose,
The gardener of the World, he goes.

THE DUMB SOLDIER

When the grass was closely mown,
Walking on the lawn alone,
In the turf a hole I found
And hid a soldier underground.

Spring and daisies came apace;
Grasses hide my hiding-place;
Grasses run like a green sea
O'er the lawn up to my knee.

Under grass alone he lies,
Looking up with leaden eyes,
Scarlet coat and pointed gun,
To the stars and to the sun.

When the grass is ripe like grain,
When the scythe is stoned again,
When the lawn is shaven clear,
Then my hole shall reappear.

I shall find him, never fear,
I shall find my grenadier;
But for all that's gone and come,
I shall find my soldier dumb.

He has lived, a little thing,
In the grassy woods of spring;
Done, if he could tell me true,
Just as I should like to do.

He has seen the starry hours
And the springing of the flowers;
And the fairy things that pass
In the forests of the grass.

In the silence he has heard
Talking bee and ladybird,
And the butterfly has flown
O'er him as he lay alone.

Not a word will he disclose,
Not a word of all he knows.
I must lay him on the shelf,
And make up the tale myself.

AUTUMN FIRES

In the other gardens
  And all up the vale,
From the autumn bonfires
  See the smoke trail!

Pleasant summer over
  And all the summer flowers,
The red fire blazes,
  The grey smoke towers.

Sing a song of seasons!
  Something bright in all!
Flowers in the summer,
  Fires in the fall!

THE GARDENER

The gardener does not love to talk,
He makes me keep the gravel walk;
And when he puts his tools away,
He locks the door and takes the key.

Away behind the currant row
Where no one else but cook may go,
Far in the plots, I see him dig,
Old and serious, brown and big.

He digs the flowers, green, red, and blue,
Nor wishes to be spoken to.
He digs the flowers and cuts the hay,
And never seems to want to play.

Silly gardener! summer goes,
And winter comes with pinching toes,
When in the garden bare and brown
You must lay your barrow down.

Well now, and while the summer stays,
To profit by these garden days,
O how much wiser you would be
To play at Indian wars with me!

HISTORICAL ASSOCIATIONS

Dear Uncle Jim, this garden ground
That now you smoke your pipe around
Has seen immortal actions done
And valiant battles lost and won.

Here we had best on tip-toe tread,
While I for safety march ahead,
For this is that enchanted ground
Where all who loiter slumber sound.

Here is the sea, here is the sand,
Here is simple Shepherd's Land,
Here are the fairy hollyhocks,
And there are Ali Baba's rocks.

But yonder, see! apart and high,
Frozen Siberia lies; where I,
With Robert Bruce and William Tell,
Was bound by an enchanter's spell.

There, then, awhile in chains we lay,
In wintry dungeons, far from day;
But ris'n at length, with might and main,
Our iron fetters burst in twain.

Then all the horns were blown in town;
And, to the ramparts clanging down,
All the giants leaped to horse
And charged behind us through the gorse.

On we rode, the others and I,
Over the mountains blue, and by
The Silent River, the sounding sea,
And the robber woods of Tartary.

A thousand miles we galloped fast,
And down the witches' lane we passed,
And rode amain, with brandished sword,
Up to the middle, through the ford.

Last we drew rein—a weary three—
Upon the lawn, in time for tea,
And from our steeds alighted down
Before the gates of Babylon.

ENVOYS

TO WILLIE AND HENRIETTA

If two may read aright
These rhymes of old delight
And house and garden play,
You two, my cousins, and you only, may.

You in a garden green
With me were king and queen,
Were hunter, soldier, tar,
And all the thousand things that children are.

Now in the elders' seat
We rest with quiet feet,
And from the window-bay
We watch the children, our successors, play.

" Time was," the golden head
Irrevocably said;
But time which none can bind,
While flowing fast away, leaves love behind.

TO MY MOTHER

You too, my mother, read my rhymes
For the love of unforgotten times,
And you may chance to hear once more
The little feet along the floor.

TO AUNTIE

Chief of our aunts—not only I,
But all your dozen of nurslings cry—
What did the other children do?
And what were childhood, wanting you?

TO MINNIE

The red room with the giant bed
Where none but elders laid their head;
The little room where you and I
Did for awhile together lie,
And, simple suitor, I your hand
In decent marriage did demand;
The great day nursery, best of all,
With pictures pasted on the wall
And leaves upon the blind—
A pleasant room wherein to wake
And hear the leafy garden shake
And rustle in the wind—
And pleasant there to lie in bed
And see the pictures overhead—
The wars about Sebastopol,
The grinning guns along the wall,
The daring escalade,
The plunging ships, the bleating sheep,
The happy children ankle-deep
And laughing as they wade;

All these are vanished clean away,
And the old manse is changed to-day;
It wears an altered face
And shields a stranger race.
The river, on from mill to mill,
Flows past our childhood's garden still;
But ah! we children never more
Shall watch it from the water-door!
Below the yew—it still is there—
Our phantom voices haunt the air
As we were still at play,
And I can hear them call and say:
" *How far is it to Babylon?* "

Ah, far enough, my dear,
Far, far enough from here—
Yet you have farther gone!
" *Can I get there by candlelight?* "
So goes the old refrain.

I do not know—perchance you might—
But only, children, hear it right.
Ah, never to return again!
The eternal dawn, beyond a doubt,
Shall break on hill and plain,
And put all stars and candles out,
Ere we be young again.

To you in distant India, these
I send across the seas,
Nor count it far across.
For which of us forgets
The Indian cabinets,
The bones of antelope, the wings of
    albatross,
The pied and painted birds and beans,
The junks and bangles, beads and screens,
The gods and sacred bells,

And the loud-humming, twisted shells?
The level of the parlour floor
Was honest, homely, Scottish shore;
But when we climbed upon a chair,
Behold the gorgeous East was there!

Be this a fable; and behold
Me in the parlour as of old,
And Minnie just above me set
In the quaint Indian cabinet!
Smiling and kind, you grace a shelf
Too high for me to reach myself.
Reach down a hand, my dear, and take
These rhymes for old acquaintance' sake.

TO MY NAME-CHILD

Some day soon this rhyming volume, if you
    learn with proper speed,
Little Louis Sanchez, will be given you to read.
Then shall you discover, that your name was
    printed down
By the English printers, long before, in London
    town.

In the great and busy city where the East and
    West are met,
All the little letters did the English printer set;
While you thought of nothing, and were still
    too young to play,
Foreign people thought of you in places far away.

Ay, and while you slept, a baby, over all the
    English lands
Other little children took the volume in their
    hands;

Other children questioned, in their homes across
  the seas:
Who was Little Louis, won't you tell us,
  mother, please?

Now that you have spelt your lesson, lay it down
  and go and play,
Seeking shells and seaweed on the sand of
  Monterey,
Watching all the mighty whalebones, lying
  buried by the breeze,
Tiny sandy-pipers, and the huge Pacific seas.

And remember in your playing, as the sea-fog
  rolls to you,
Long ere you could read it, how I told you
  what to do;
And that while you thought of no one, nearly
  half the world away
Some one thought of Louis on the beach of
  Monterey!

TO ANY READER

Whether upon the garden seat
You lounge with your uplifted feet
Under the May's whole Heaven of blue;
Or whether on the sofa you,
No grown up person being by,
Do some soft corner occupy!
Take you this volume in your hands
And enter into other lands,
For lo! (as children feign) suppose
You, hunting in the garden rows,
Or in the lumbered attic, or
The cellar—a nail-studded door
And dark, descending stairway found
That led to kingdoms underground:
There standing, you should hear with ease
Strange birds a-singing, or the trees
Swing in big robber woods, or bells
On many fairy citadels:

There passing through (a step or so
Neither mamma nor nurse need know!)
From your nice nurseries you would pass
Like Alice through the Looking-Glass
Or Gerda following Little Ray,
To wondrous countries far away.
Well, and just this volume can
Transport each little maid or man,
Presto, from where they live away
Where other children used to play.
As from the house your mother sees
You playing round the garden trees,
So you may see, if you will look
Through the windows of this book,
Another child, far, far away,
And in another garden, play.
But do not think you can at all,
By knocking on the window, call
That child to hear you. He intent
Is all on his play-business bent.
He does not hear; he will not look,
Nor yet be lured out of his book.
For, long ago, the truth to say,
He has grown up and gone away,
And it is but a child of air
That lingers in the garden there.

INDEX OF FIRST LINES

	page
A birdie with a yellow bill	100
A child should always say what's true	40
All night long, and every night	38
All round the house is the jet black night	116
All the names I know from nurse	159
At evening when the lamp is lit	139
Birds all the sunny day	157
Bring the comb and play upon it!	75
Chief of our aunts—not only I	181
Children, you are very little	83
Come up here, O dusty feet	105
Dark brown is the river	55
Dear Uncle Jim, this garden ground	173
Down by a shining water well	128
Every night my prayers I say	66
Faster than fairies, faster than witches	106
From breakfast on all through the day	61
Great is the sun and wide he goes	161
How do you like to go up in a swing	98
I have a little shadow that goes in and out with me	63
I saw you toss the kites on high	79
I should like to rise and go	49
I woke before the morning, I was happy all the day	69
If two may read aright	179
In the other gardens	168
In winter I get up at night	35

	page
It is very nice to think	36
Last, to the chamber where I lie	118
Late lies the wintry sun a-bed	108
Little Indian, Sioux or Crow	86
My bed is like a little boat	93
My tea is nearly ready	91
O it's I that am the captain of a tidy little ship	125
Of speckled eggs the birdie sings	52
Over the borders, a sin without pardon	80
Smooth it slides upon its travel	101
Some day soon this rhyming volume	187
Summer fading, winter comes	131
The coach is at the door at last	112
The friendly cow, all red and white	76
The gardener does not love to talk	171
The lamps now glitter down the street	143
The lights from the parlour and kitchen shone out	71
The moon has a face like the clock in the hall	97
The rain is raining all around	41
The red room with the giant bed	183
The sun is not a-bed when I	89
The world is so full of a number of things	77
These nuts that I keep in the back of the nest	133
Three of us afloat in the meadow by the swing	42
Through all the pleasant meadow-side	111
Up into the cherry-tree	44
We built a ship upon the stairs	54
What are you able to build with your blocks?	137
When at home alone I sit	145
When children are playing alone on the green	121
When I am grown to man's estate	53
When I was sick and lay a-bed	59
When I was down beside the sea	37
When the bright lamp is carried in	115
When the golden day is done	151
When the grass was closely mown	165
Whenever Auntie moves around	58
Whenever the moon and stars are set	47
Whether upon the garden seat	189
You, too, my mother, read my rhymes	180